play guitar with...

classic songs

play guitar with...
classic songs

Wise Publications
part of The Music Sales Group
London/New York/Paris/Sydney/Copenhagen/Berlin/Madrid/Hong Kong/Tokyo

Published by
Wise Publications
14-15 Berners Street, London W1T 3LJ, UK

Exclusive Distributors:
Music Sales Limited
Distribution Centre, Newmarket Road,
Bury St Edmunds, Suffolk IP33 3YB, UK

Music Sales Pty Limited
20 Resolution Drive,
Caringbah, NSW 2229, Australia

Order No. AM1001407
ISBN 978-1-84938-666-1
This book © Copyright 2011 Wise Publications,
a division of Music Sales Limited.

www.musicsales.com

Edited by Tom Farncombe
Music Engraved by Paul Ewers Music Design Limited

All Right Now
Guitars: Arthur Dick
Bass: Tom Farncombe
Drums: Noam Lederman
Keyboards: Jonas Persson

Livin' On A Prayer
Guitars: Arthur Dick
Bass: Paul Townsend
Drums: Noam Lederman
Keyboards: Paul Honey

Recorded and mixed by Jonas Persson

Don't Stop Believin', Hold The Line, More Than A Feeling,
Since You've Been Gone, Sweet Home Alabama
Guitars, Bass and Keyboards: Tom Fleming
Drums: Dave Cottrell

Recorded and mixed by Tom Fleming

CD mastered by Will Moore and Jonas Persson

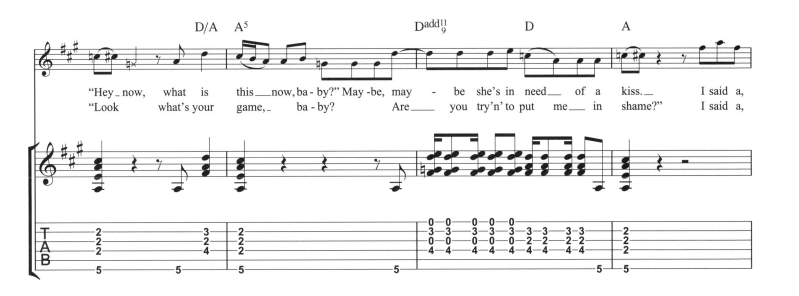

"Hey_ now, what is this_ now, ba-by?" May-be, may - be she's in need_ of a kiss._ I said a,
"Look what's your game,_ ba-by? Are_ you try'n' to put me_ in shame?" I said a,

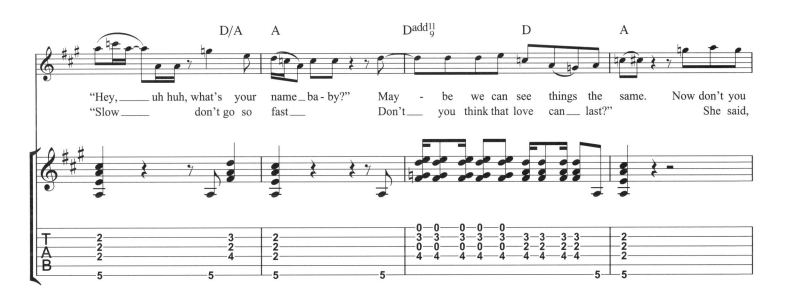

"Hey,_____ uh huh, what's your name_ ba-by?" May - be we can see things the same. Now don't you
"Slow_____ don't go so fast_____ Don't_ you think that love can_ last?" She said,

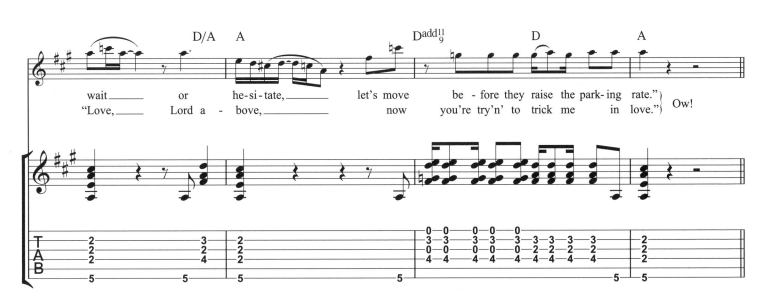

wait_____ or he-si-tate,_____ let's move be - fore they raise the park-ing rate." } Ow!
"Love,_____ Lord a - bove,_____ now you're try'n' to trick me in love." }

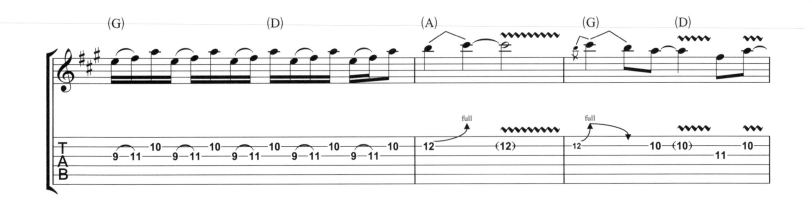
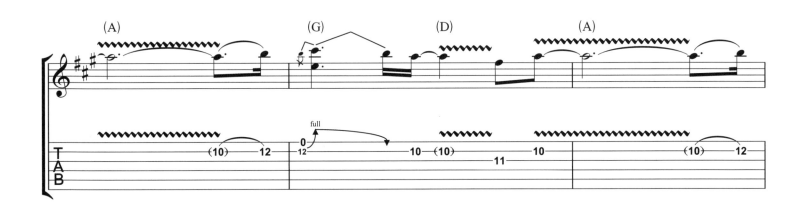
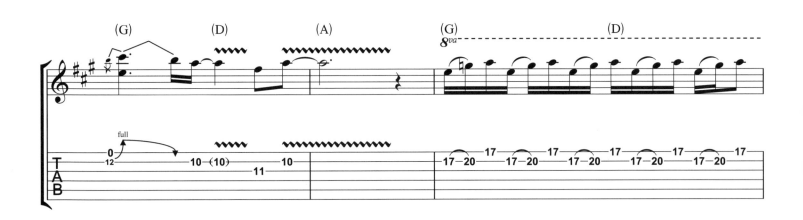
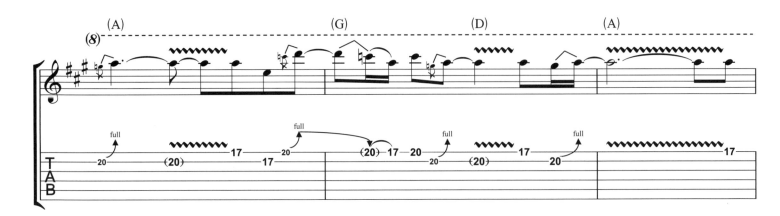

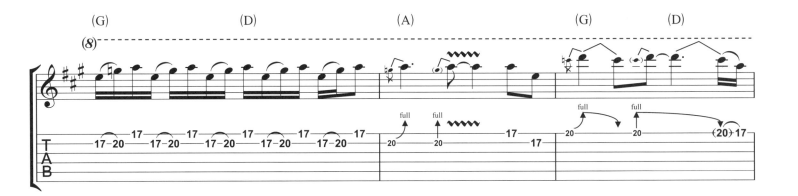

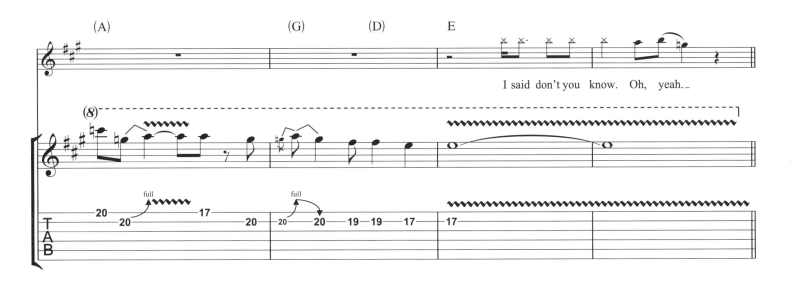

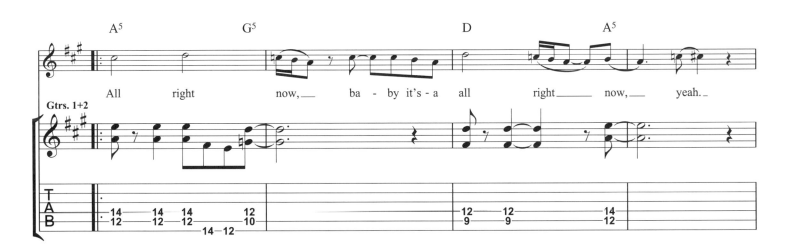

Repeat with ad lib. vocals to fade

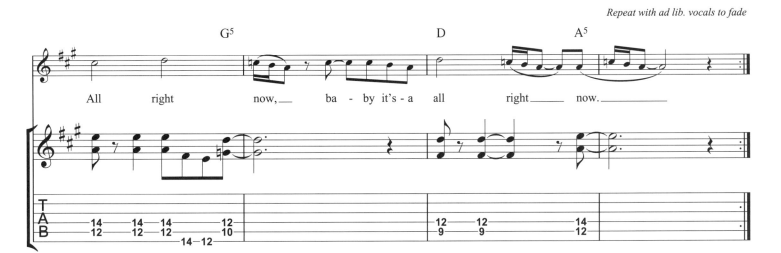

15

don't stop believin'

Words & Music by Steve Perry, Neal Schon & Jonathan Cain

Full performance demo: track 2
Backing only: track 9

Intro
2 bar count in:

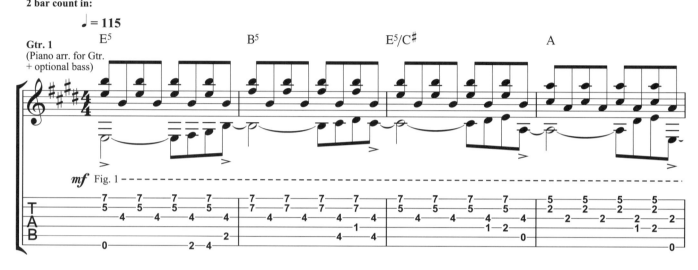

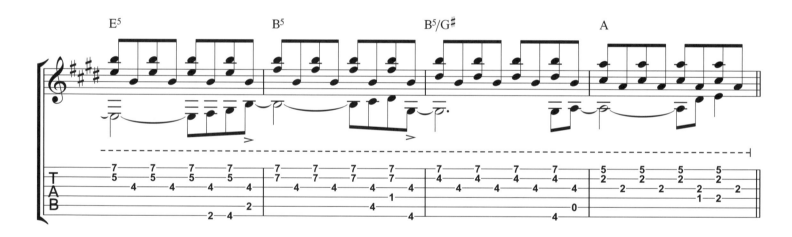

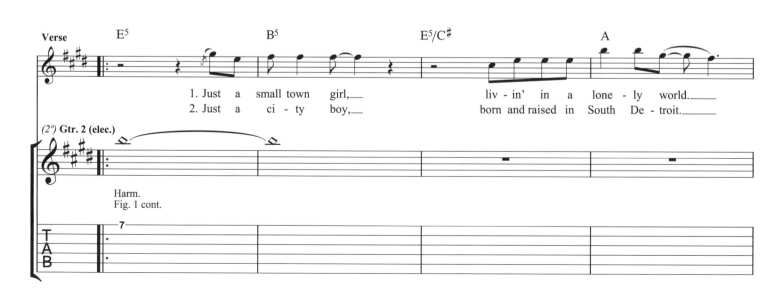

Verse

1. Just a small town girl,___ liv - in' in a lone - ly world.___
2. Just a ci - ty boy,___ born and raised in South De - troit.___

She took the mid-night train_ go-in' a - ny - where.___

He took the mid-night train_ go-in' a - ny - where.___

*reverse rake between bridge and tail piece

Play Gtr. 3 part

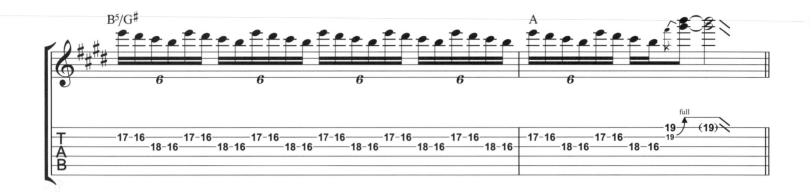

Verse
(Fig. 1 cont.)

3. A sing-er in a smok-y room.__ The smell of wine and cheap per-fume.____

For a smile__ they can share the night;__ It goes on and on____ and on____ and on.____

Bridge

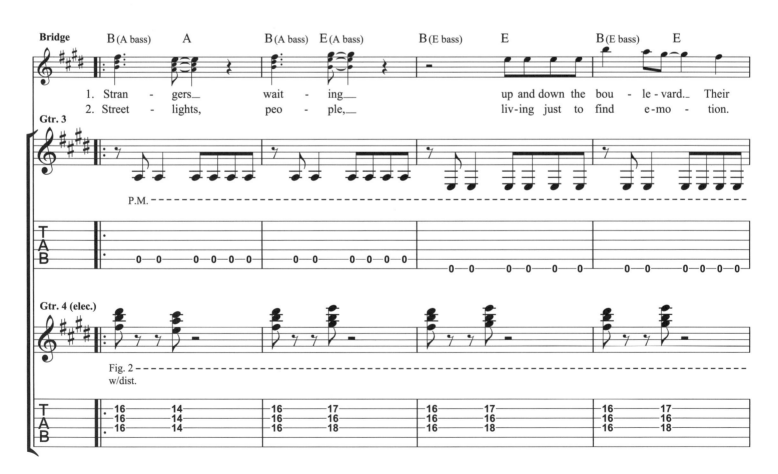

1. Stran - gers____ wait - ing____ up and down the bou - le - vard.__ Their
2. Street - lights, peo - ple,__ liv-ing just to find e-mo - tion.

Gtr. 3

P.M.

Gtr. 4 (elec.)

Fig. 2
w/dist.

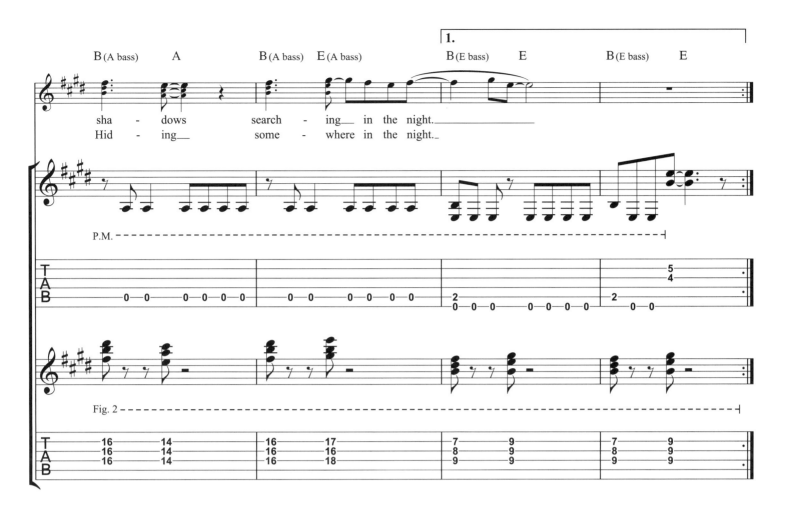

sha - dows   search - ing___ in the night._____
Hid - ing___   some - where in the night.__

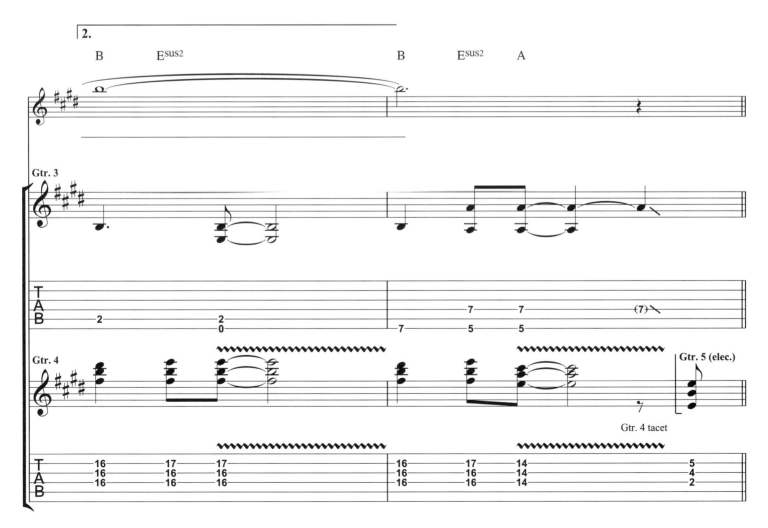

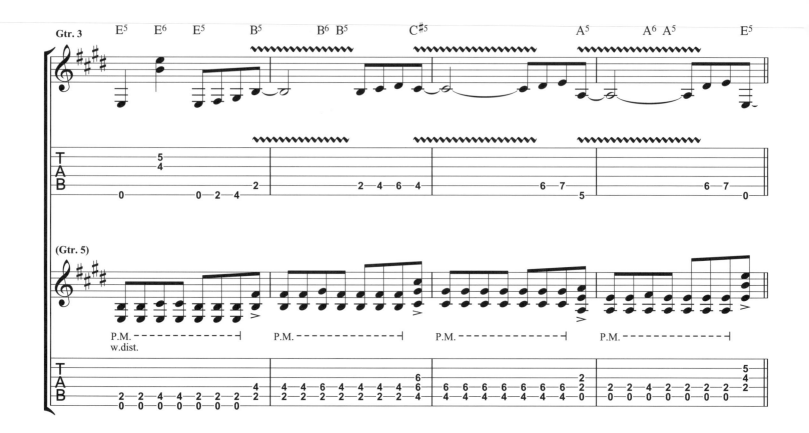

4. Work-in' hard_ to get my fill.__ Ev-'ry-bo-dy wants a thrill.__

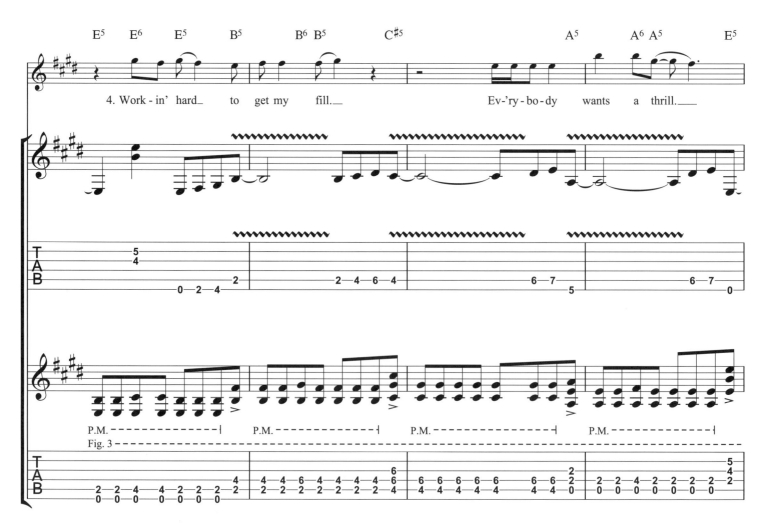

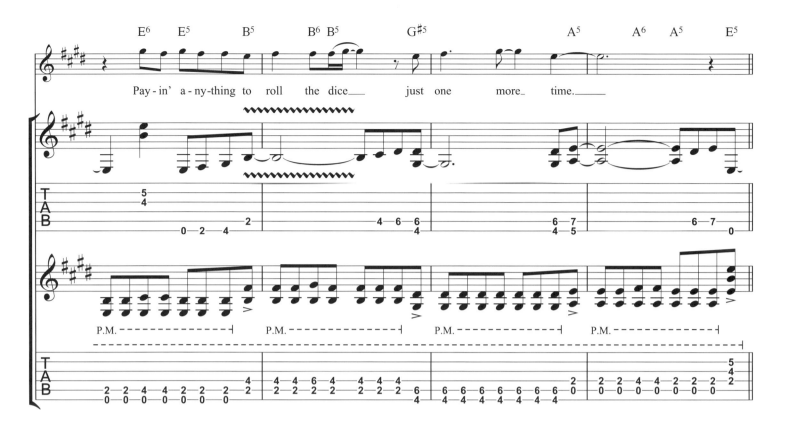

Pay-in' a-ny-thing to roll the dice___ just one more___ time.___

P.M. P.M. P.M. P.M.

5. Some will win,___ some will lose,___ some were born to sing the blues.___

Gtr. 5 plays Fig. 3 *ad lib.*

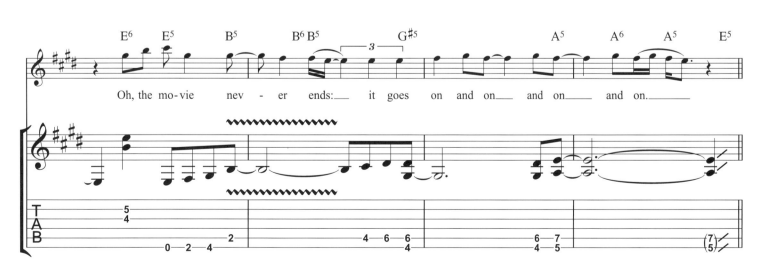

Oh, the mo-vie nev-er ends:___ it goes on and on___ and on___ and on.___

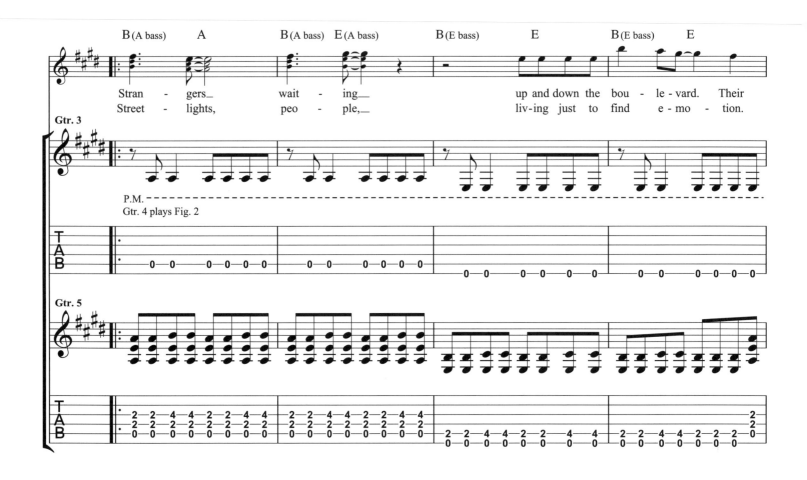

Stran - gers___ wait - ing___ up and down the bou - le - vard. Their
Street - lights, peo - ple,___ liv-ing just to find e - mo - tion.

Gtr. 3

P.M. -
Gtr. 4 plays Fig. 2

Gtr. 5

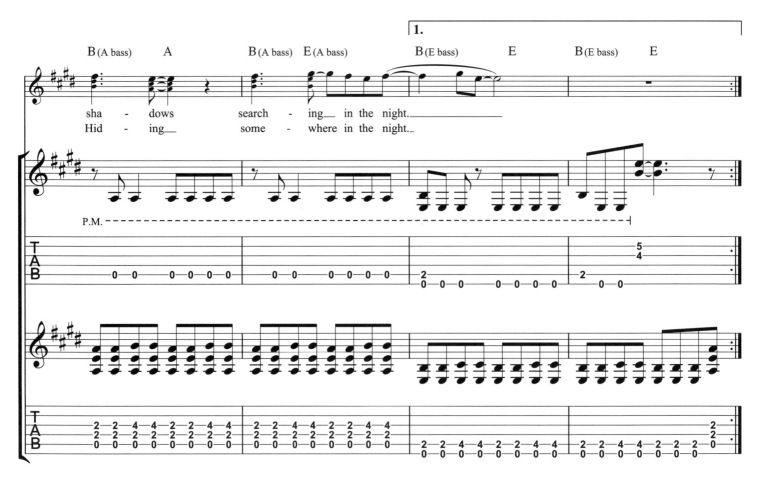

sha - dows search - ing___ in the night.___
Hid - ing___ some - where in the night.___

P.M. -

24

hold the line

Words & Music by David Paich

Full performance demo: track 3
Backing only: track 10

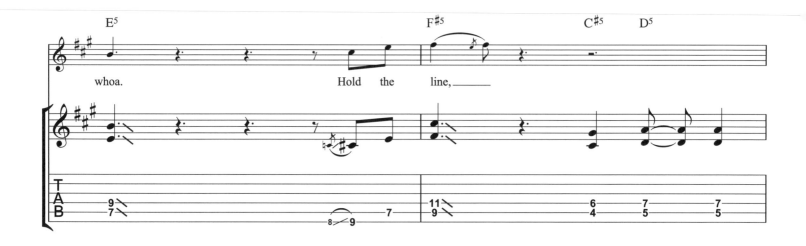

whoa. Hold the line,_____

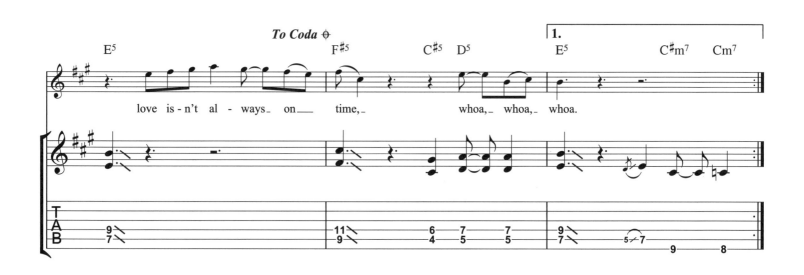

love is-n't al - ways_ on ___ time,_ whoa,_ whoa,_ whoa.

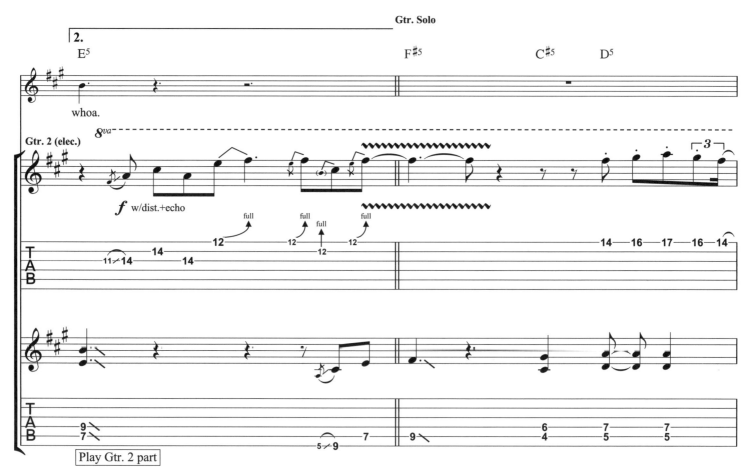

whoa.

Play Gtr. 2 part

* notes in parenthesis indicate echo repeats

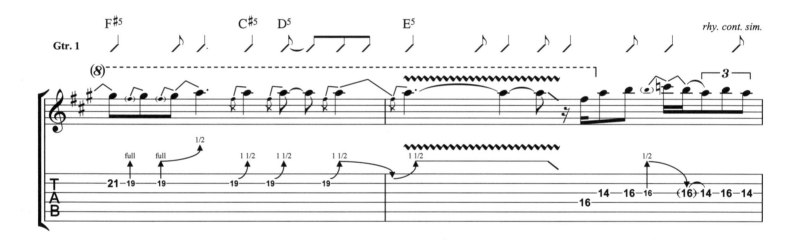

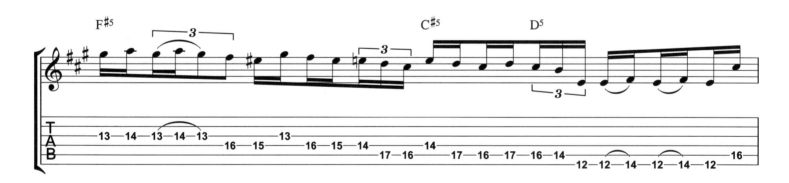

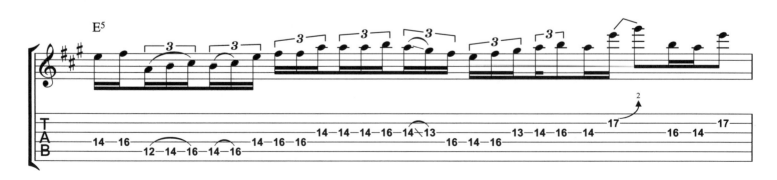

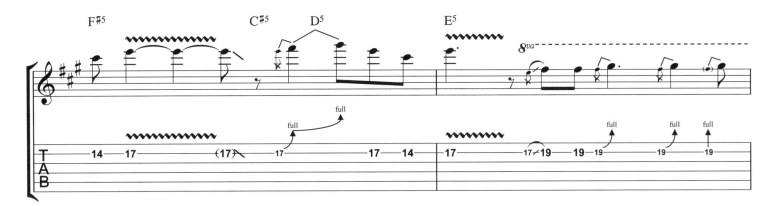

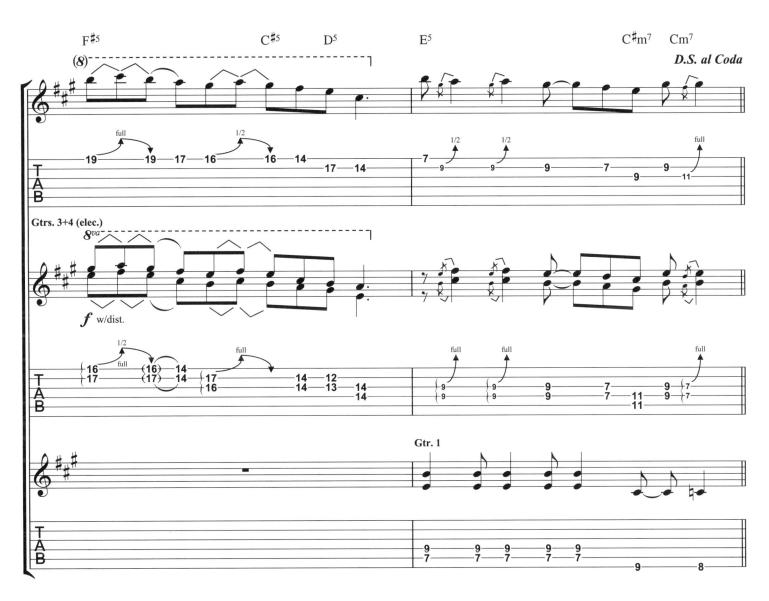

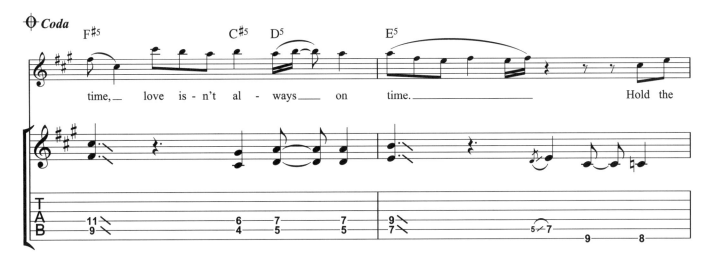

time,____ love is-n't al - ways____ on time._____ Hold the

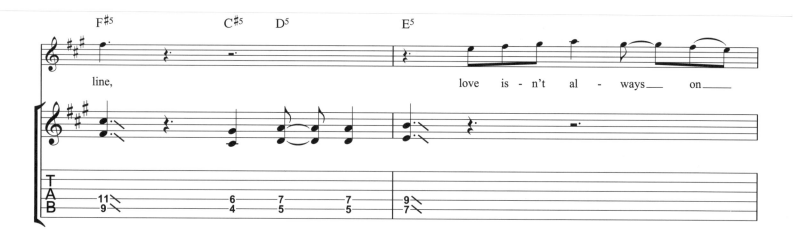

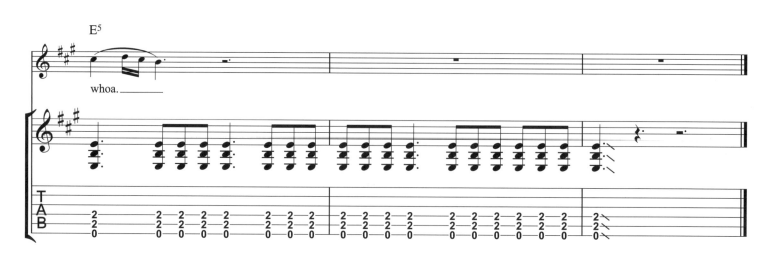

livin' on a prayer

Words & Music by Jon Bon Jovi, Richie Sambora & Desmond Child

Full performance demo: track 4
Backing only: track 11

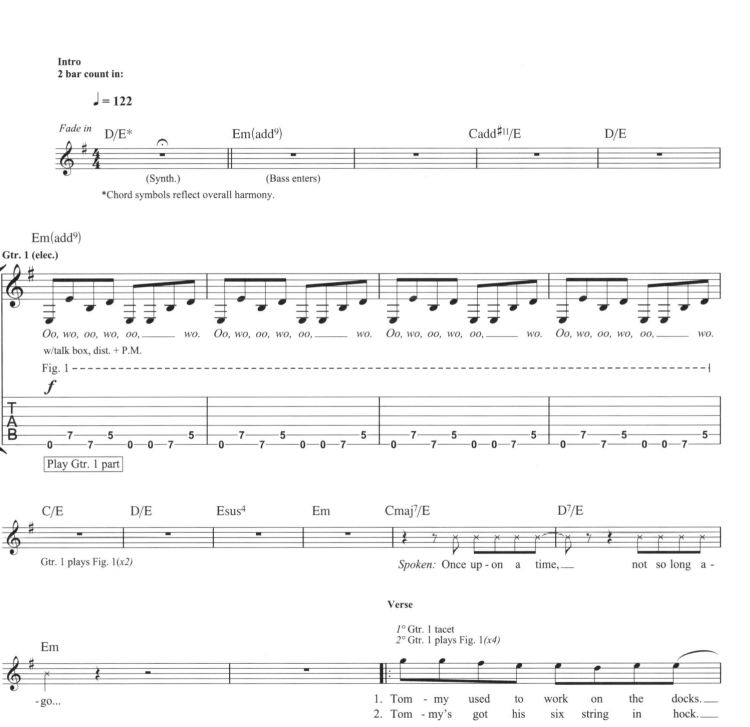

33

more than a feeling

Words & Music by Tom Scholz

Full performance demo: track 5
Backing only: track 12

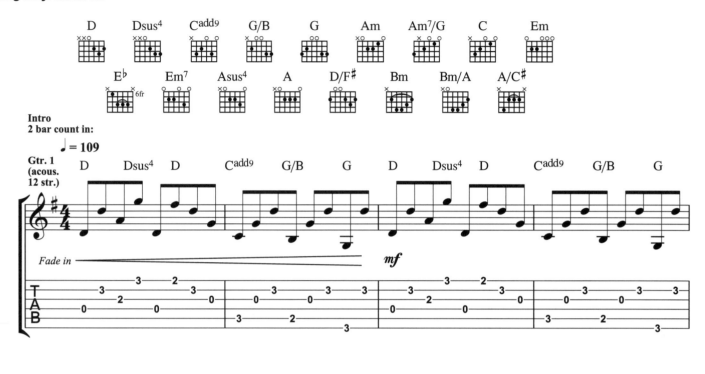

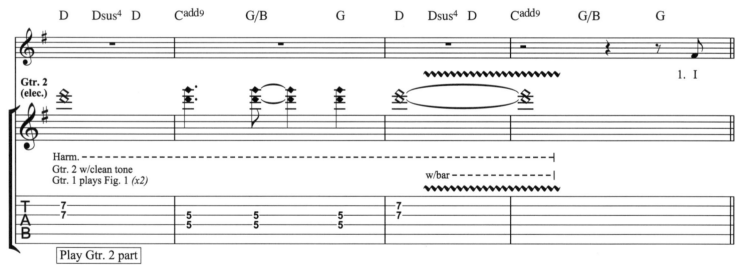

Play Gtr. 2 part

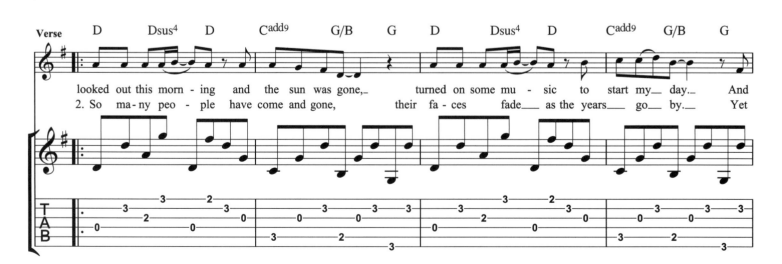

Verse

looked out this morn-ing and the sun was gone,___ turned on some mu-sic to start my___ day.___ And

2. So ma-ny peo-ple have come and gone, their fa-ces fade___ as the years___ go___ by.___ Yet

lost my - self____ in a fa - mi - liar song,____ I closed my eyes____ and I slipped a - way.____
I still re - call____ as I wan - der on,____ as clear as the sun____ in the sum - mer sky.____

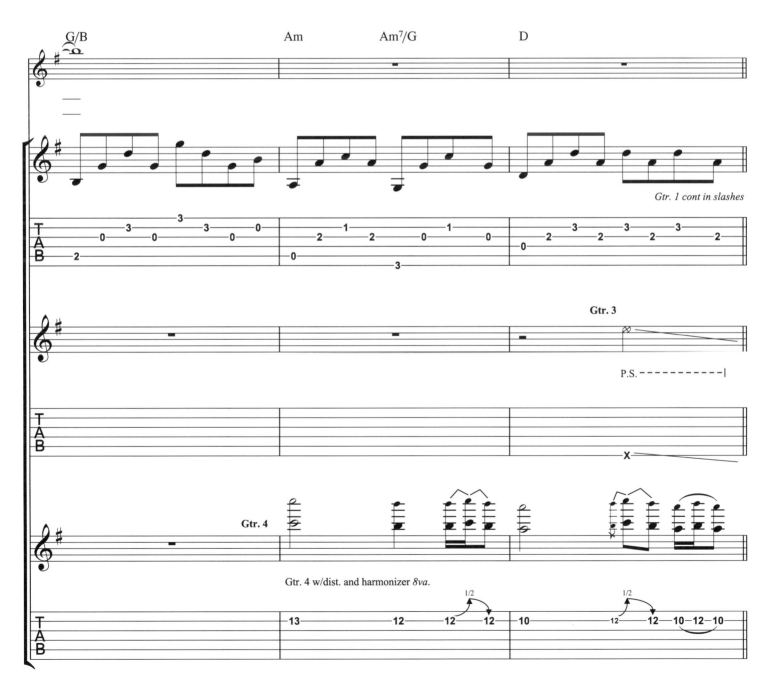

Gtr. 1 cont in slashes

Gtr. 3

P.S. -----------|

Gtr. 4

Gtr. 4 w/dist. and harmonizer *8va.*

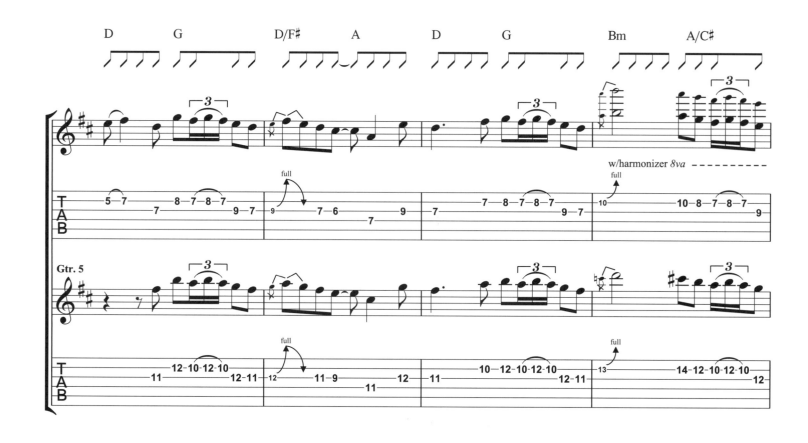

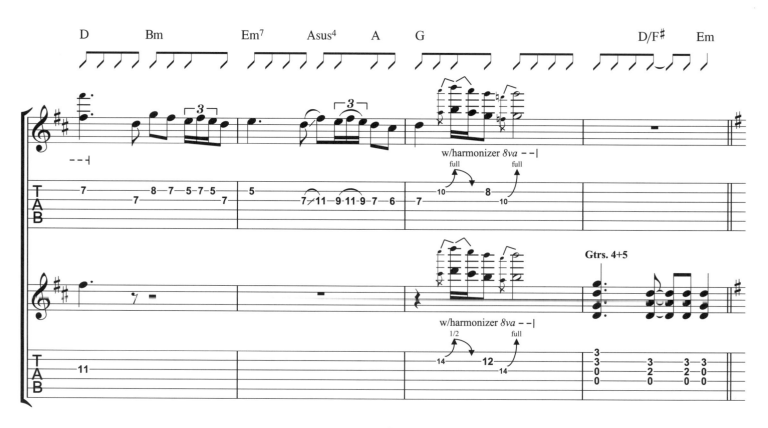

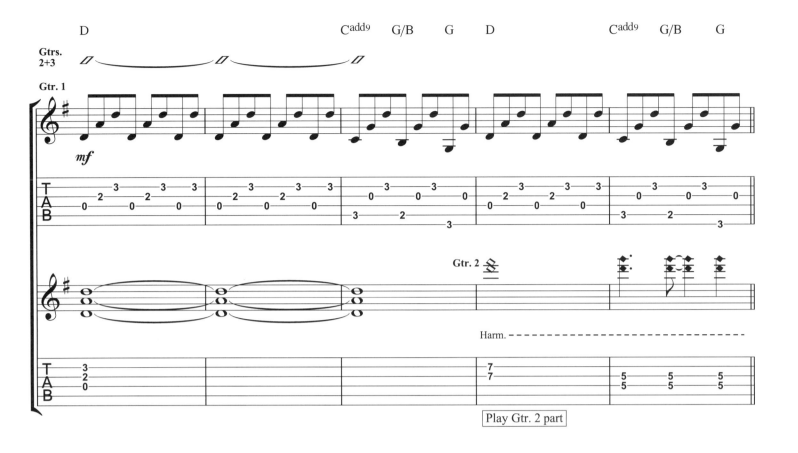

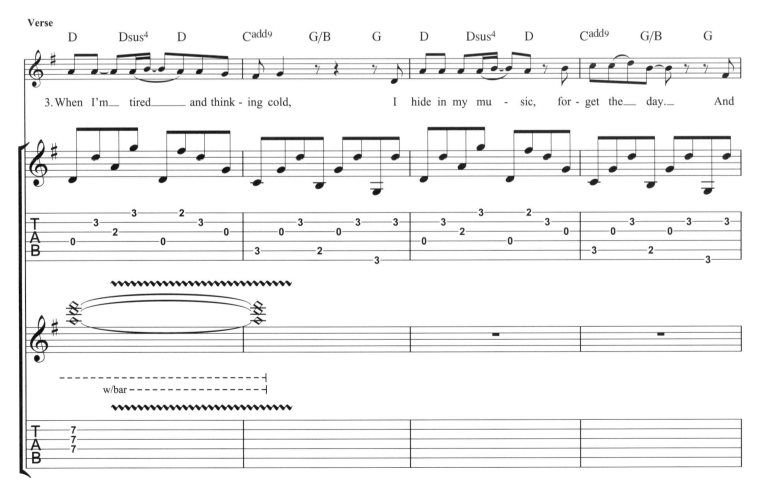

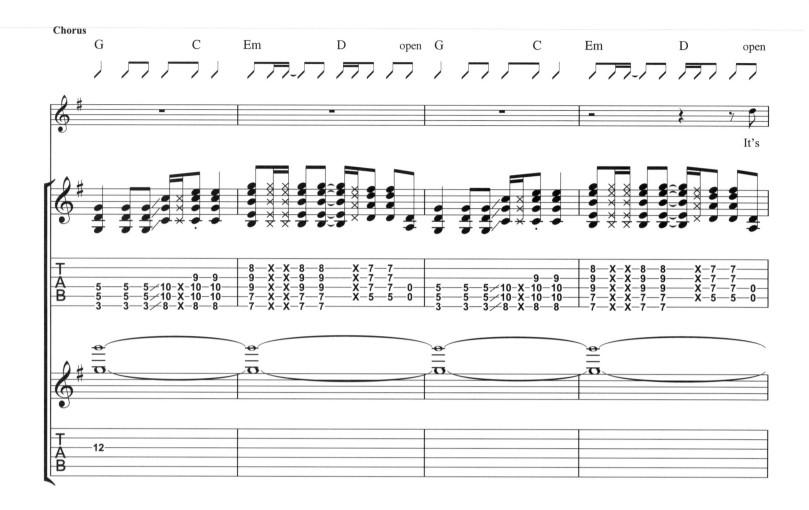

Play Gtr. 3 part

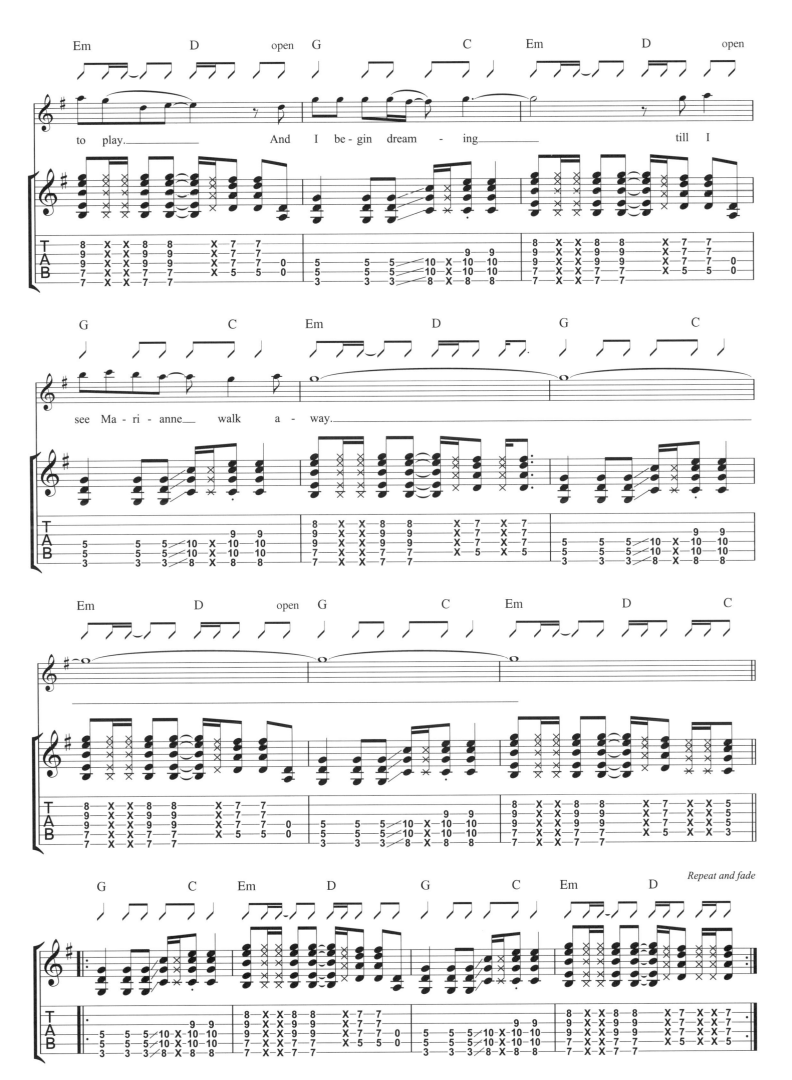

since you've been gone

Words & Music by Russ Ballard

Full performance demo: track 6
Backing only: track 13

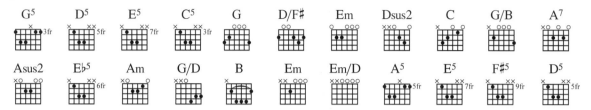

Intro
2 bar count in:

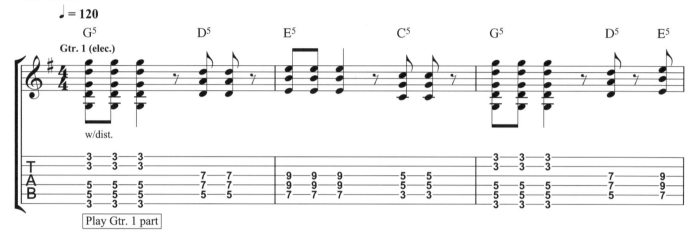

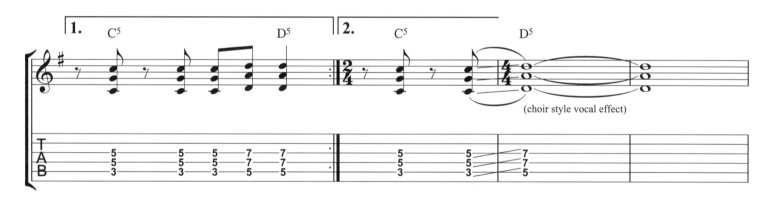

(choir style vocal effect)

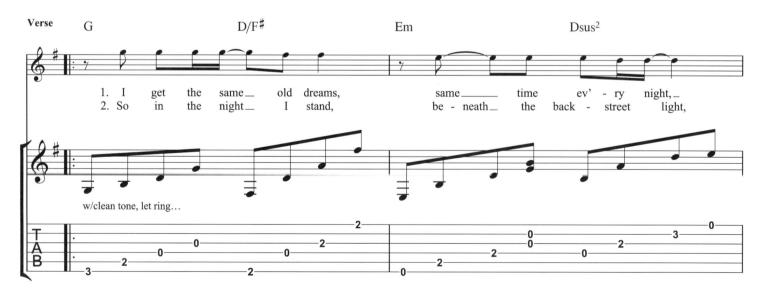

1. I get the same old dreams, same time ev'ry night,
2. So in the night I stand, beneath the back-street light,

w/clean tone, let ring…

48

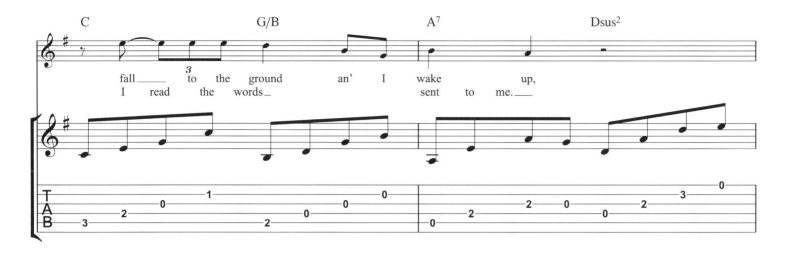

C   G/B   A^7 Dsus^2

fall___ to the ground an' I wake up,
I read the words___ sent to me.___

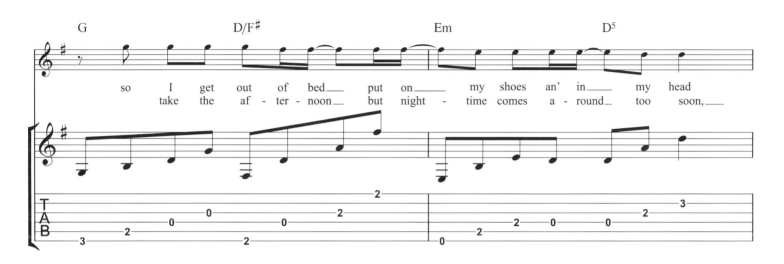

G   D/F$\sharp$ Em   D^5

so I get out of bed___ put on___ my shoes an' in___ my head
take the af - ter - noon___ but night - time comes a - round___ too soon,___

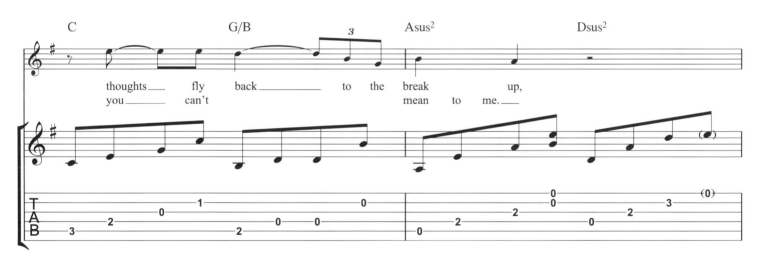

C   G/B   Asus^2 Dsus^2

thoughts___ fly back___ to the break up,
you___ can't   mean to me.___

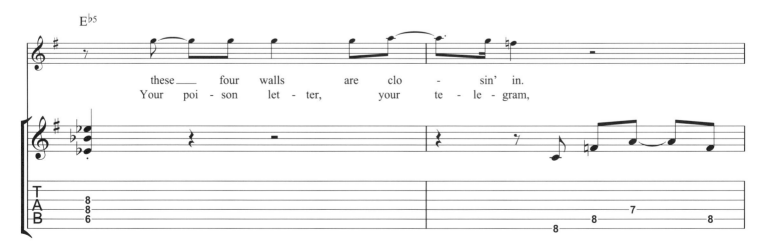

E$^{\flat 5}$

these___ four walls are clo - sin' in.
Your poi - son let - ter, your te - le - gram,

49

Look at the fix you've ___ put ___ me ___ in.
just goes to show you don't give ___ a ___ damn.

Since you've been gone, ___ since you've been gone ___ I'm out of my head, can't take ___ it.

Could I be wrong, ___ but since you've been gone ___

you cast a spell, ___ so ___ break ___ it. Oh ___

50

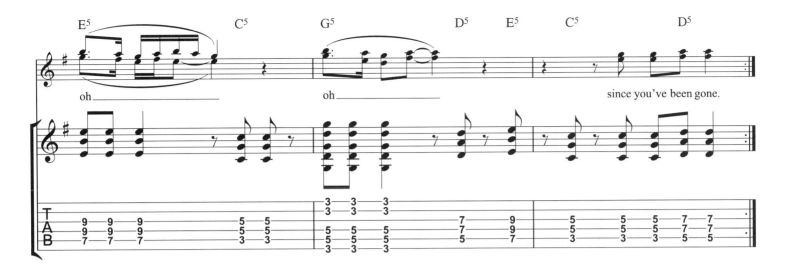

oh _____ oh _____ since you've been gone.

Bridge **Half time feel**
Gtr. 1

w/clean tone
Fig. 1...

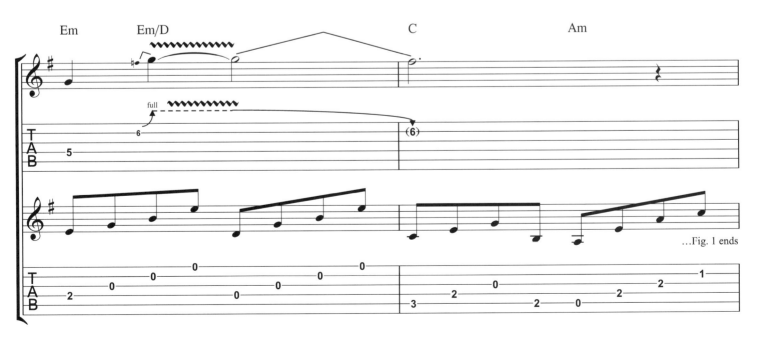

...Fig. 1 ends

sweet home alabama

Words & Music by Ronnie Van Zant, Ed King & Gary Rossington

Full performance demo: track 7
Backing only: track 14

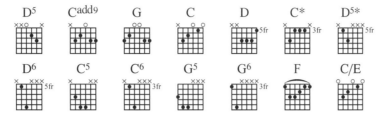

Intro
2 bar count in:

♩ = 100

Turn it up.

Play Gtr. 1 part

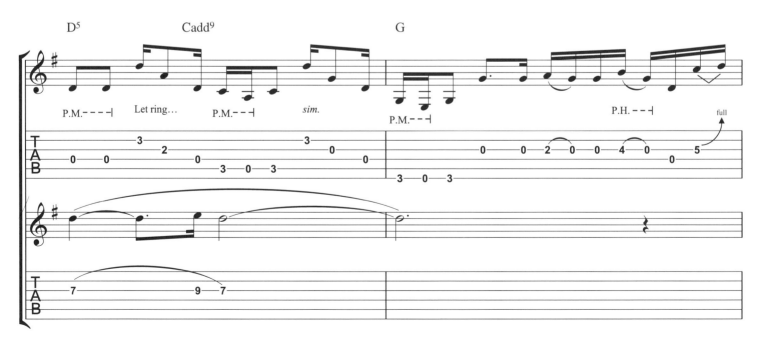

55

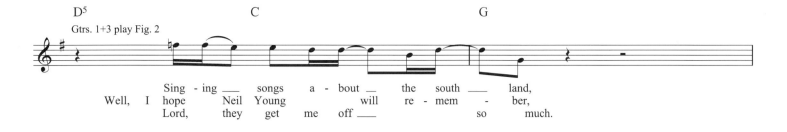

D⁵   C   G

Gtrs. 1+3 play Fig. 2

Sing - ing ___ songs a - bout ___ the south ___ land,
Well, I hope Neil Young will re - mem - ber,
Lord, they get me off ___ so much.

1.

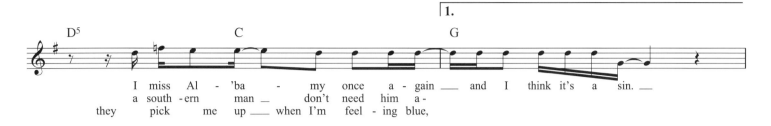

D⁵   C   G

I miss Al - 'ba - my once a - gain ___ and I think it's a sin. ___
a south - ern man ___ don't need him a -
they pick me up ___ when I'm feel - ing blue,

Interlude

Gtrs. 1+3

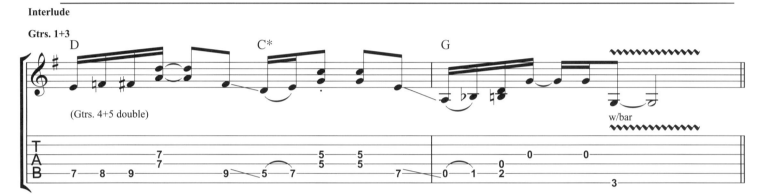

(Gtrs. 4+5 double)

w/bar

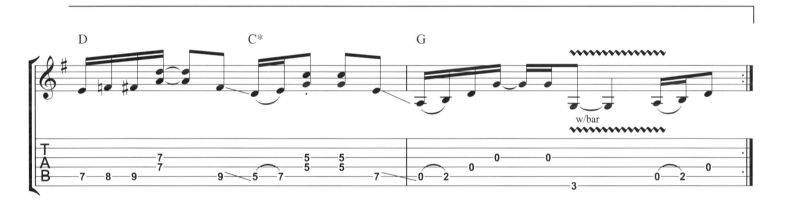

w/bar

2, 3.

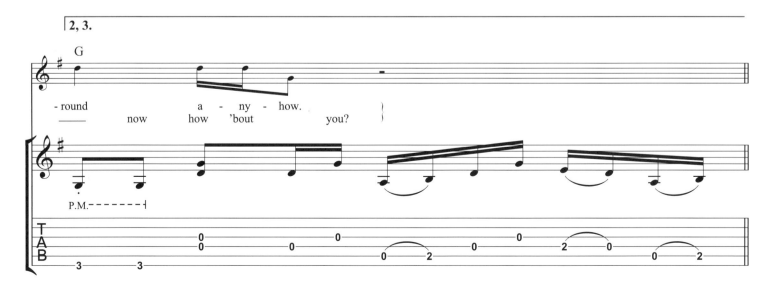

- round now a - ny - how.
___ now how 'bout you?

P.M.- - - - - - - -

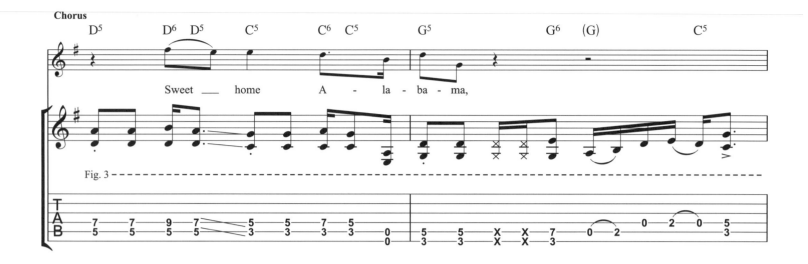

Sweet ___ home A - la - ba - ma,

Fig. 3

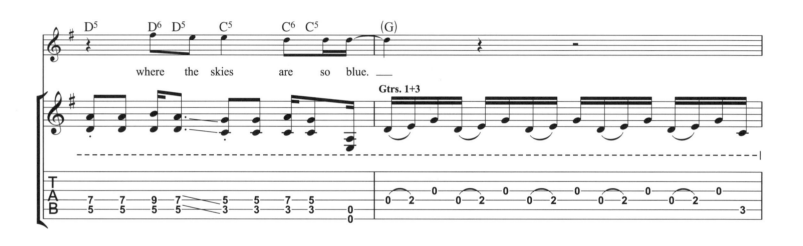

where the skies are so blue. ___

Gtrs. 1+3

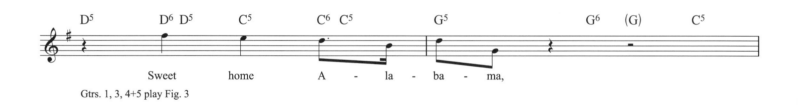

Sweet home A - la - ba - ma,

Gtrs. 1, 3, 4+5 play Fig. 3

To Coda ⊕

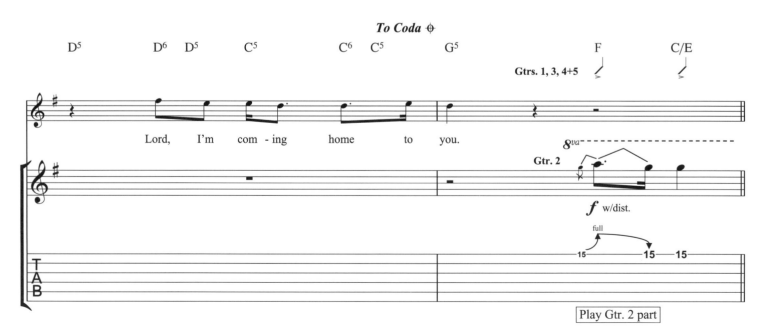

Lord, I'm com - ing home to you.

Gtrs. 1, 3, 4+5

Gtr. 2

f w/dist.

Play Gtr. 2 part

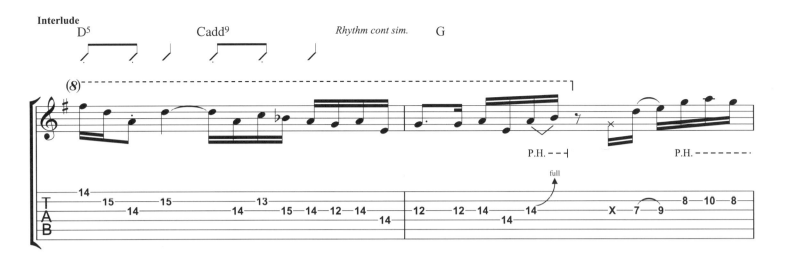

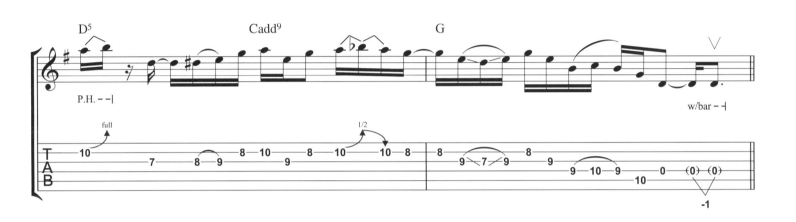

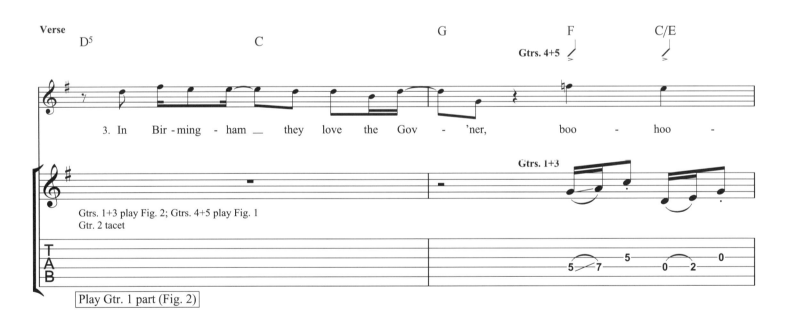

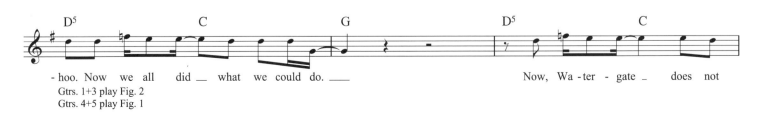

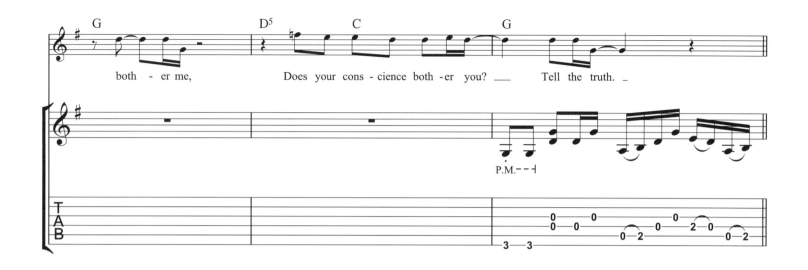

both - er me, Does your cons - cience both - er you? __ Tell the truth. __

P.M.----┤

Chorus

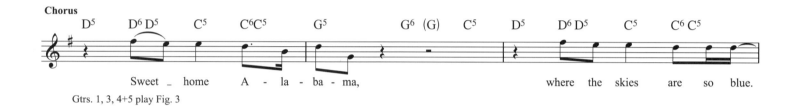

Sweet __ home A - la - ba - ma, where the skies are so blue.

Gtrs. 1, 3, 4+5 play Fig. 3

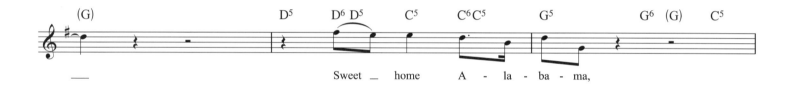

__ Sweet __ home A - la - ba - ma,

Gtrs. 1, 3, 4+5

Lord, I'm com - ing home to you. Here I come, A - la - ba - ma.

Gtr. Solo

Rhythm cont. sim.

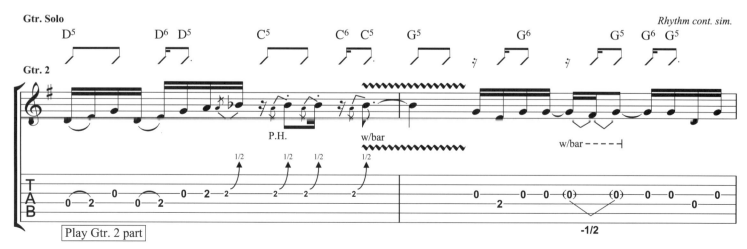

Gtr. 2

P.H.

w/bar

w/bar -----┤

Play Gtr. 2 part

-1/2

60

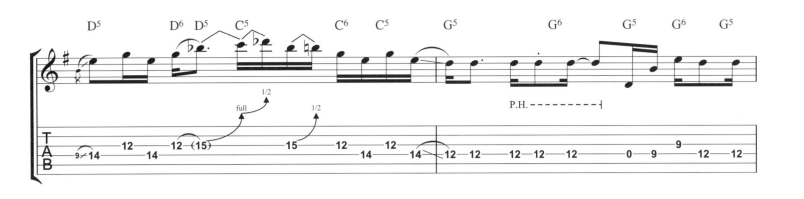
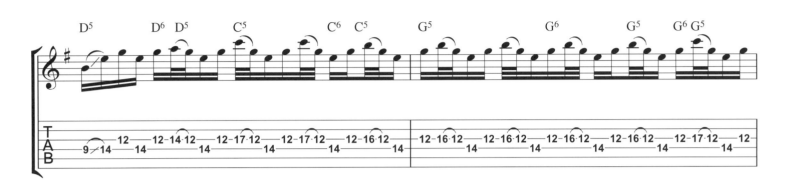
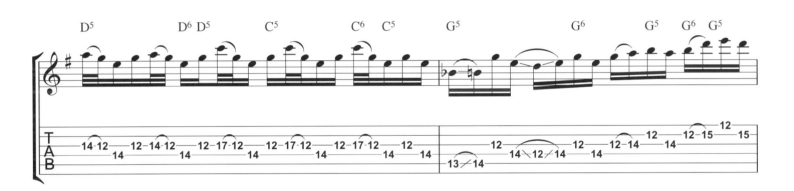
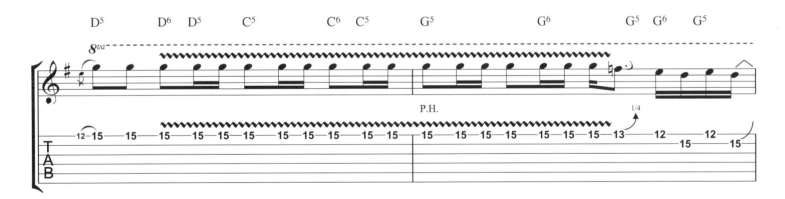
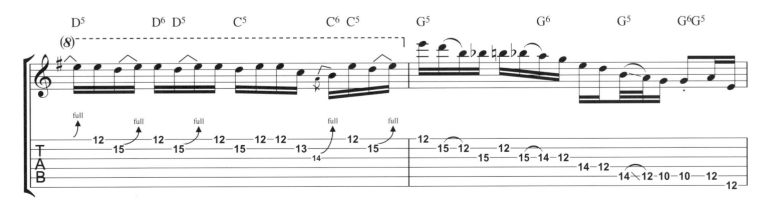

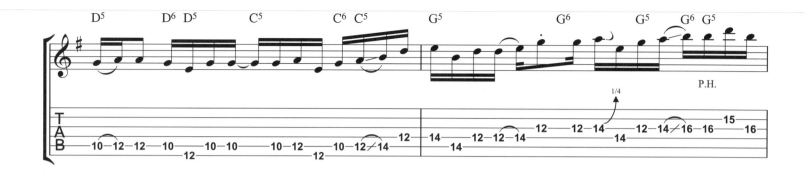

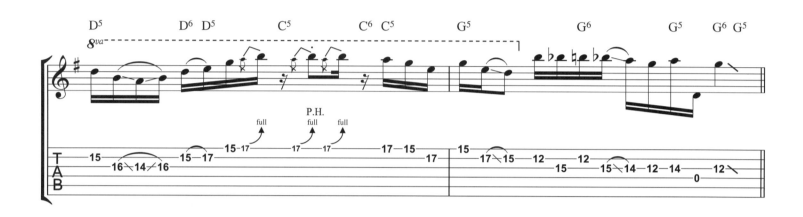

Interlude

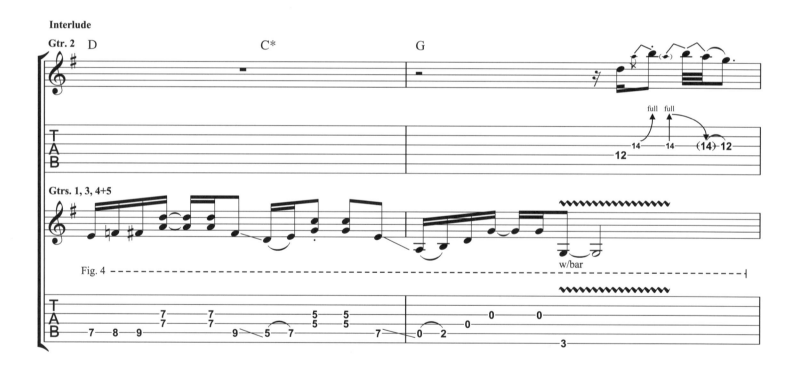

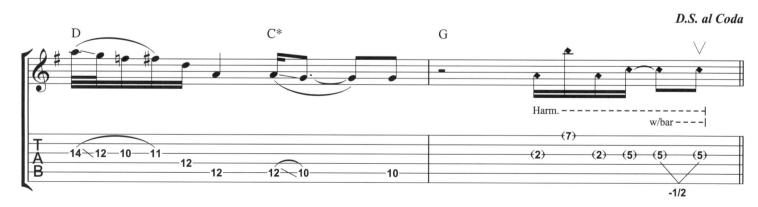

CD track listing

Full instrumental performances (with guitar)...

1 **all right now**
(Rodgers/Fraser) Blue Mountain Music Limited

2 **don't stop believin'**
(Perry/Schon/Cain)
Alfred Music Publishing Company Incorporated/
Sony/ATV Music Publishing (UK) Limited

3 **hold the line**
(Paich) Sony/ATV Music Publishing (UK) Limited

4 **livin' on a prayer**
(Jovi/Sambora/Child) Universal Music Publishing Limited/
Sony/ATV Music Publishing (UK) Limited

5 **more than a feeling**
(Scholz) Sony/ATV Music Publishing (UK) Limited

6 **since you've been gone**
(Ballard) Complete Music Limited

7 **sweet home alabama**
(Van Zant/King/Rossington) Universal/MCA Music Limited

Backing tracks (without guitar)...

8 **all right now**

9 **don't stop believin'**

10 **hold the line**

11 **livin' on a prayer**

12 **more than a feeling**

13 **since you've been gone**

14 **sweet home alabama**

To remove your CD from the plastic sleeve,
lift the small lip to break the perforation.
Replace the disc after use for convenient storage.